Ex Libris

_____

_____

_____

_____

ISBN 0-439-33168-4

Illustrations copyright © 2000 by Christopher Bing. All rights reserved. Published by Scholastic Inc., 555 Broadway, New York, NY 10012, by arrangement with Handprint Books. SCHOLASTIC and associated logos are trademarks and/or registered trademarks of Scholastic Inc.

2 11 10 9 8 7 6 5 4 3 2 1   1 2 3 4 5 6/0

Printed in Mexico

49

First Scholastic printing, September 2001

Mudville SU

VOLUME XIV **JUNE 3, 1888**

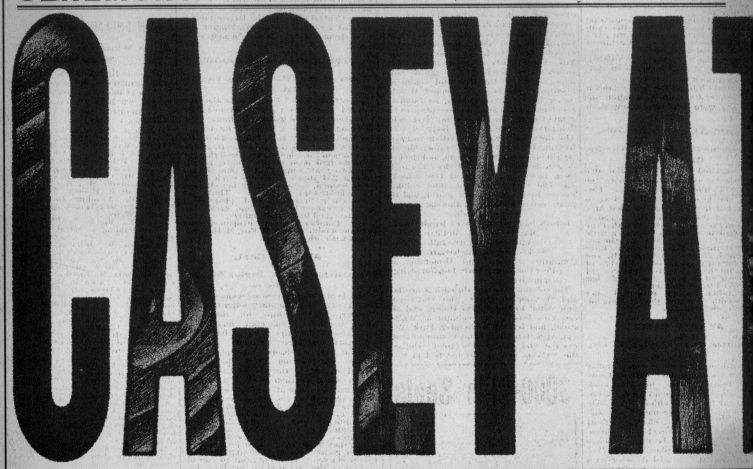

CASEY AT

A BALLAD OF THE REPUBLI

REPORTED BY ERNEST L. THAYE

THIS BOOK IS DEDICATED to all those children of spring who have found moments of heaven in the smell of a freshly mowed ballpark beneath their feet, a well-worn and oiled glove on their hand, the crack of a bat on a ball and the umpire's bellow of "Play Ball," but most especially Bill, Gil, Sean, Patrick, Ryan, Ryan O., Matt, Matty, William, Biff, and Christian.

This book is for my son Christian, for giving me back a love thought lost for the game of baseball, and the cherished gift of watching the greatest catch in the history of baseball on a warm spring night in 1995. And for my wife, Wendy, and our daughters, Amy and Tessa, for their patience while I juggled furiously, standing on one foot.

SCHOLASTIC INC.

New York Toronto

London Auckland

Sydney Mexico City

New Delhi

Hong Kong

Buenos Aires

A NOTE TO THE READER...

...about the second signature on the illustrations which appears in the lower right hand corner of each spread.

Until late in the 19th century, the metal plates from which newspaper illustrations were printed were prepared by hand by craftsmen known as engravers. Their skill lay in translating the light and shadows of the artist's original drawing on paper into the precise, unforgiving line cut into zinc or copper plates. Some of these engravers were merely crude copyists, others displayed keen talent and an interpretive gift which often augmented the artist's intention (and even covered his

flaws). Over time, several of engravers became famous in own right, and their work w sought after as that of the a whose images they reproduce was custom for the original ar name to appear in the lower of the engraving; the engra name, when allowed, appeare the lower right.

(Continued on front end pape

Monitor

LATE EDITION **TWO CENTS**

EXTRA!
MIGHTY CASEY TO LEAD MUDVILLE TO VICTORY

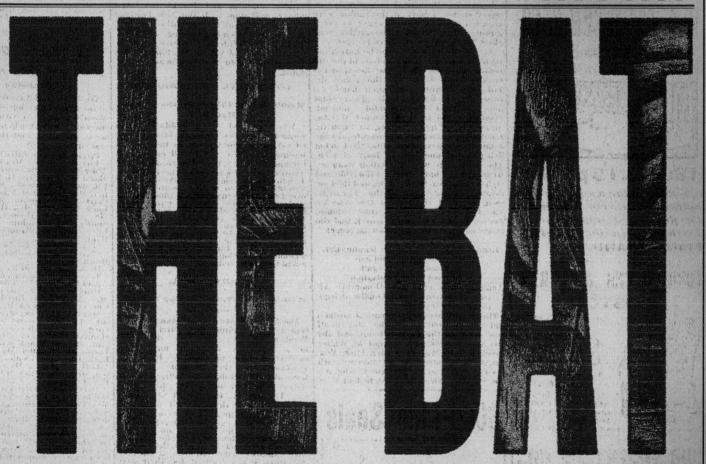

THE BAT

SUNG IN THE YEAR 1888
ILLUSTRATED BY CHRISTOPHER BING

THANKS
& ACKNOWLEDGEMENTS

Martin Gardner's brilliant and entertaining *The Annotated Casey the Bat* is the source for the title and stanzas in this version of *Casey*, which is exactly how it was first published Sunday morning, June 3rd, 1888 in the *San Francisco Examiner*.

Wallace Tripp's wonderfully illustrated version (Coward, McCann and Geoghegan, Inc., New York) in 1978 was/is the inspiration for this version and should be print again.

This book (and those to follow) would not have happened without the moral support and a helpful word on my behalf by Dr. Henry Louis Gates Jr.

Carl Brandt, my agent, for listening to the helpful word and stepping out of his usual arena and into another on my behalf, and being more interested in my getting it right than the many deadlines that came and went (due to family needs), and the bottom line (and his son, who has fought for me in another artistic arena for years helping to support my venture into this one, none of us knowing, until recently, of our professional relationships with each other).

Christopher Franceschelli, my publisher, who backed this rookie and believed in this book since he first saw sketches eight years ago.

My wife, Wendy, and our children, who have to beware of the bear in the barn, but they keep feeding it anyway, and spend so much time going without.

SUPPORT
YOUR LOCAL, REGIONAL, AND NATIONAL LIBRARIES
AND THE PEOPLE WHO WORK IN THEM. THEY ARE OUR COLLECTIVE TREASURE!

My parents who keep a hope and faith (in me) alive that would put Boston Red Sox or Chicago Cubs fans to shame.

My in-laws who actually admit that I'm family, and Gil Barrett (my brother-in-law) who put up with my turning him from the best mechanic in New England into THE model for Casey. Finding the world of modeling too dull, he has happily returned to being the best mechanic in New England.

Joseph and Princes Fludd who gave me friendship, food, and shelter one very cold and snowy night on my way to do research at the Baseball Hall of Fame.

The Baseball Hall of Fame in Cooperstown, New York and all the people who work in their photo

(Continued on front end papers)

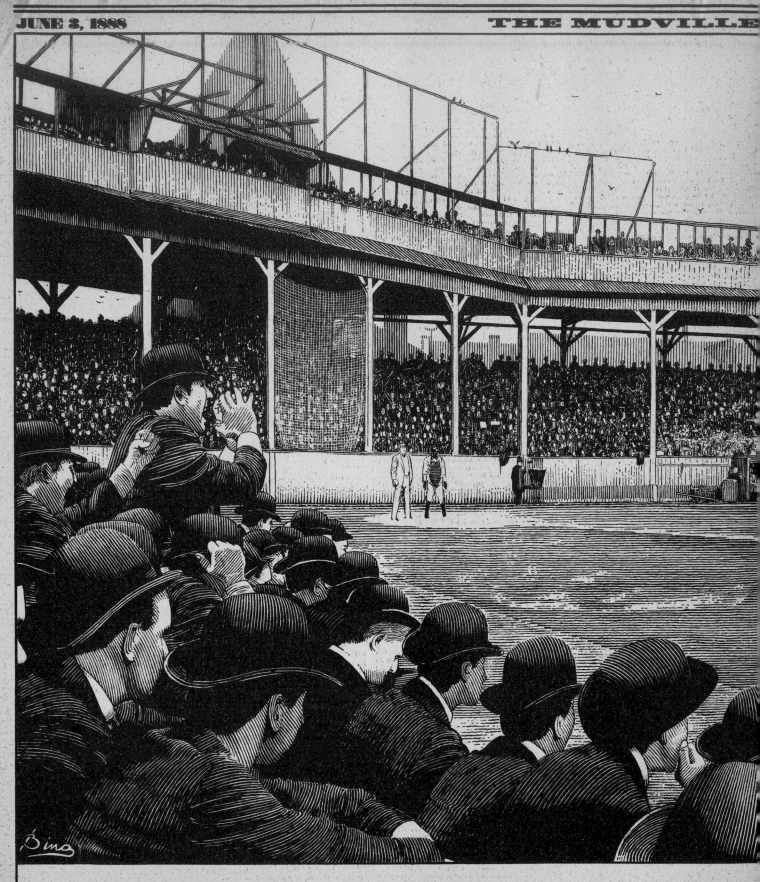

The outlook wasn't brilliant for the Mudville nine that day;
The score stood four to two with but one inning more to play.

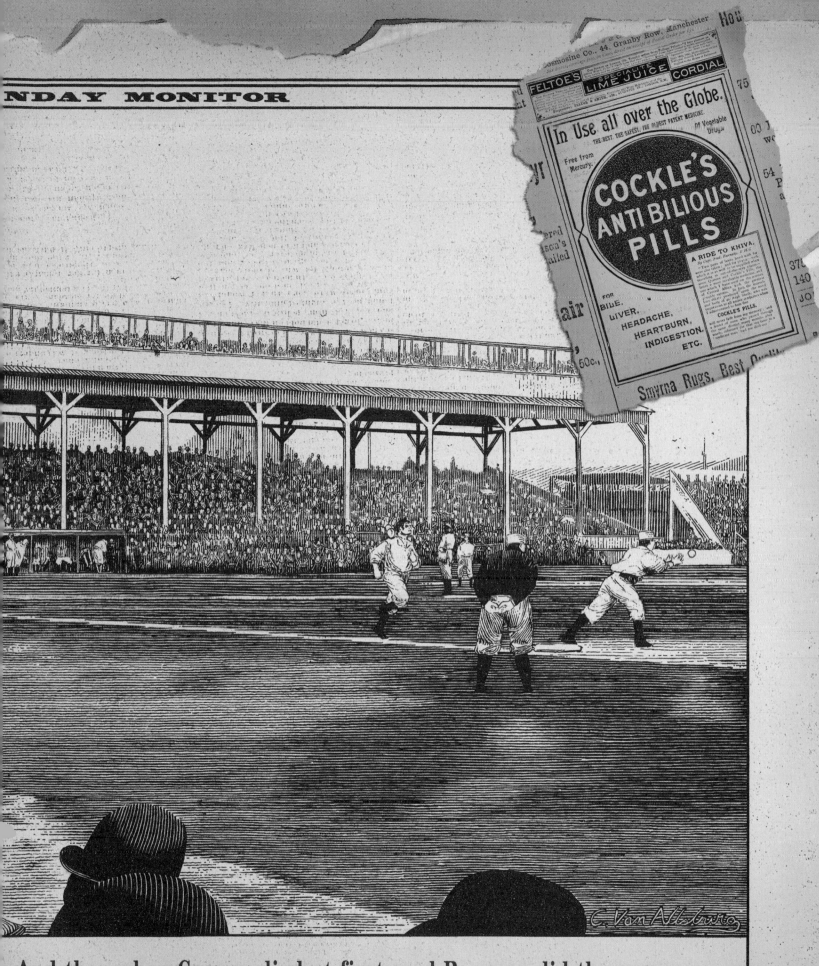

C. Van Alstyne

And then when Cooney died at first, and Barrows did the same,
A sickly silence fell upon the patrons of the game.

A straggling few got up to go in deep despair. The rest
Clung to that hope which springs eternal in the human breast;

rdo- anse and for myself I accept it with loyalty and in that faith."

Debut of American Singers.
(Copyrig)
LONDON, June 2.— Howard Paul introduced two young American vocalists at the concert in St. James Hall last evening.

man Scott as an enemy of labor, as a dangerous person to the welfare of society and the industrial progress of America, and as a bitter enemy of organized labor.

SIXTY-SIX LASTERS QUIT.

Stowe, Bills & Hawley's Union Men Refuse to Work with Non-Unionists.

Arthur had paid remarkable deference, breaking the Indiana slate in order to fetch him to Washington, nevertheless served in two departments, and yet was able to make his address for Blaine, while Arthur was sulking under his defeat.

The silly plea that a convention of common sense men must decide against anybody whom the mugwumps do not insult and

man. It would be a confession that his ticket had been unsuccessful. In not the cases and while I know that who will vote for him don't like Blaine, there is nothing else to be done.

William Armstrong, postmaster of land, an old Democrat, remarked to Judge Thurman: "The Ohio delegates a few votes, I think, for Black; some for Stevenson, and a small number

They thought if only Casey could but get a whack at that—
We'd put up even money now with Casey at the bat.

**The Mills Bill and Its Advocates De-
nounced by Organized Labor.**

PITTSBURG, June 2.—At the meeting of
the Trades' Assembly of Western Pennsyl-
vania, representing 50,000 organized work-
men tonight, resolutions were unanimously
adopted condemning the Mills bill and all

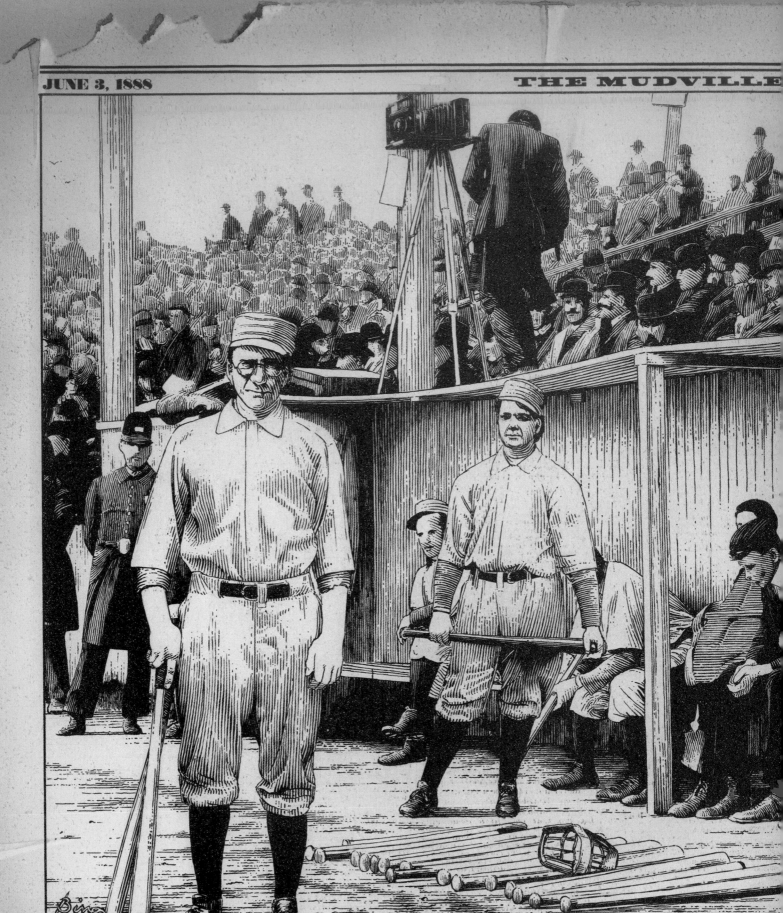

But Flynn preceded Casey, as did also Jimmy Blake,
And the former was a lulu and the latter was a cake;

SURGING FANS SPARK NEAR RIOT
SCORE CAST IN DOUBT WHEN BALL ROLLS INTO CROWD
MANAGERS AND CITY OFFICIALS RENEW CRY FOR BUILDING OF OUTFIELD FENCES

Richloam—Saturday, June 2

Martin Stone's slam into left looked to be a solid double for the Mudville nine in yesterday afternoon's game against the Richloam Roosters. Then the ball hit an obstruction in the grass and began rolling towards the crowd watching from the sidelines. Some twenty Mudville fans crossed onto the field, placed the ball into protective custody and physically prevented Regis Smallwood, the Rooster's leftfielder, from apprehending the ball.

Richloam fans were understandably incensed and exercised swift revenge, attacking the visiting Mudville fans with a flurry of walking sticks. At least one Mudville fan was seen hobbling off the field with a bloodied shirt and weakened eye. Only the quick action of the local constab-

MAYOR STONE VOICES OUTRAGE

The incident prompted Mayor Sam Stone to make a renewed call for the erection of a wall separating fans from the field. While such a barrier would be a novelty to the game—rumor has it that something of the sort has been built in New York—it is hoped that this action might lead to greater crowd safety and less confusion on the field. More than one fan, however, was heard to say that an artificial barricade would severely curtail the enjoyment of the and might mear dance.

T.B. Dowan

So upon that stricken multitude grim melancholy sat,
For there seemed but little chance of Casey's getting to the bat.

THE NATIONAL SPORTS REPORTER &
GAZETTE

THE PROUD VOICE OF THE GENTLEMAN ATHLETE
AND AMATEUR SPORTSMAN THROUGHOUT THE LAND

PUBLISHED EVERY MONDAY FROM
CHICAGO, ILLINOIS MAY 21, 1888

EDITORIAL

WE NOTE with increasing concern the barbaric practice of using only a single ball throughout the nine innings of play in a game of baseball. In this modern day, this would appear to us to be at the least unhygienic if not outright dangerous. Even the casual spectator will have noticed that by the third or fourth inning the stitching of the ball has likely been frayed and the very leather cover is flapping uselessly in the wind.

The likelihood of this defect leading to wild pitches and random hops drastically increase ballplayers' chances of being severely injured. Indeed, the dirt and grime which encases the ball after even a half hour's play renders it so difficult to see that tragedy is nigh on unavoidable.

Given that bas[e]
quality an[d]

[...]eballs of high [...] exemplary economy are available from such purveyors of sporting goods as Messrs Spalding and others, we can only urge that one ball per game rule be retired at the earliest possible instance. The very health of our players depends on it.

Base Balls.
At Manufacturers' Prices.

Our base balls are the best in the market and are guaranteed regulation weight and size. Our League balls are all warranted to stand a full game which is a new market claims for this very best balls that they [...]

OUR LEAGUE BALL

But Flynn let drive a single, to the wonderment of all,
And Blake, the much despis-ed, tore the cover off the ball;

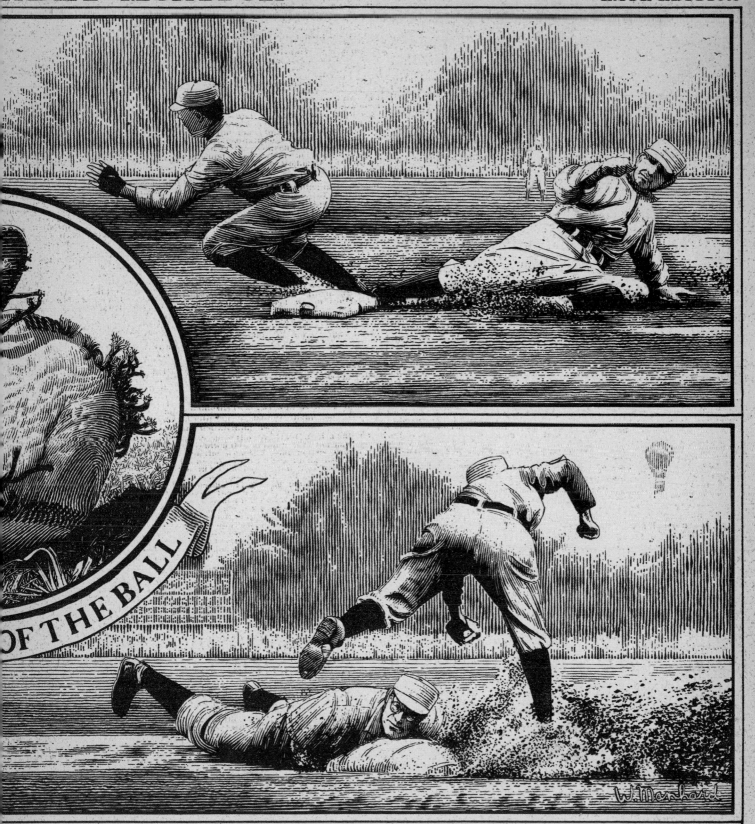

And when the dust had lifted, and the men saw what had occurred,
There was ~~Johnnie~~ safe at second and Flynn a-hugging third.

Jimmy

of Tax Reduction
now pending in Congress should be men-
tioned in the platform. By such people it
is thought to be sufficient squarely to in-
dorse the message f the President and
earnestly urge upon C gress the execution
of the princ ple. The New York platform
is really liked by Mr. Cleveland bet-
fer than that of any

PROOFREADER SOUGHT
THE MUDVILLE MONITOR seeks proofreader for immediate hire due to last
incumbent's sudden departure. The successful
candidate shall possess an exquisite command
of the language, display meticulous attention
to detail while working to extreme deadlines,
be impervious to the bustle of a cacophonous

in their power.

Kansas Men Favor Gresham.
TOPEKA, Kan., June 2.—A canvass of the
18 delegates from Kansas to the Chicago
convention since Mr. Plaine's last
letter shows that Gresham is the
personal preference of the m
One delegate is for Deney

Bing

Then from 5,000 throats and more there rose a lusty yell;

It rumbled through the valley, it rattled in the dell;

It knocked upon the mountain and recoiled upon the flat,
For Casey, mighty Casey, was advancing to the bat.

There was ease in Casey's manner as he stepped into his place;
There was pride in Casey's bearing and a smile on Casey's face.

And when, responding to the cheers, he lightly doffed his hat,
No stranger in the crowd could doubt 'twas Casey at the bat.

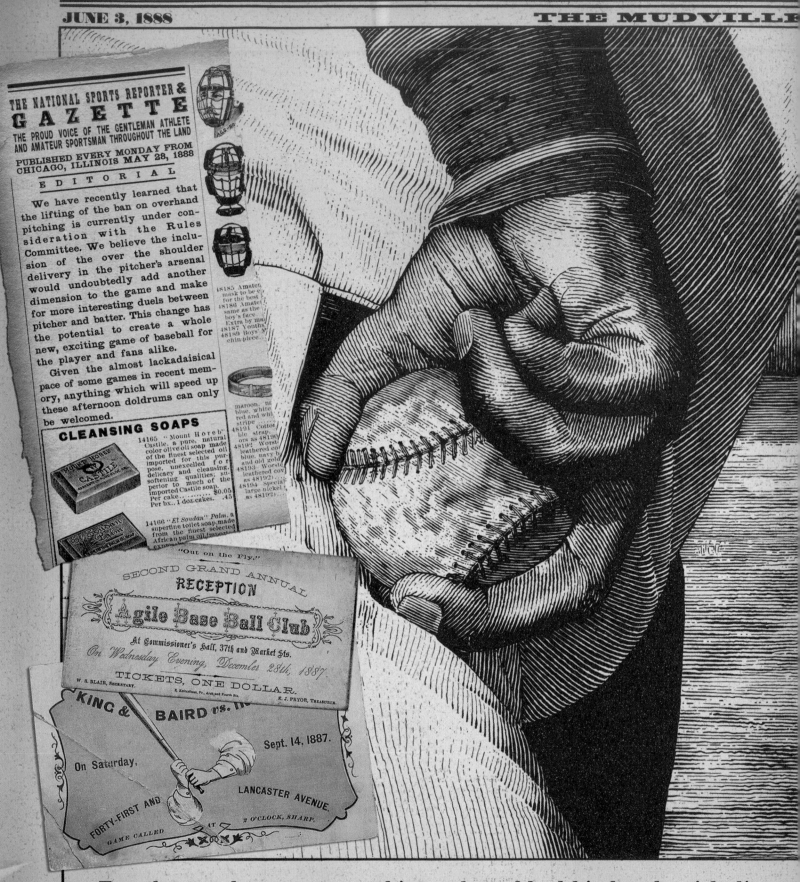

Ten thousand eyes were on him as he rubbed his hands with dirt;
Five thousand tongues applauded when he wiped them on his shirt.

THE NATIONAL SPORTS REPORTER &

GAZETTE EDITION

THE PROUD VOICE OF THE GENTLEMAN ATHLETE
AND AMATEUR SPORTSMAN THROUGHOUT THE LAND

PUBLISHED EVERY MONDAY FROM
CHICAGO, ILLINOIS APRIL 9, 1888

EDITORIAL

PANSIES IN THE (OUT)FIELD

The hoots and cat calls of "Mama's boy," "Cake" and "Lulu" often heard from the sidelines of late are the fans' justified response to the recent introduction of the ball glove to the great American pastime. They justifiably see this move as a disgrace-perhaps the first step in the calculated and tragic emasculation of the game. Blisters and swollen hands, once

Base Ball Gloves.
48149 Special Baseman's Glove, heavy oil tanned goat skin, extra heavy padded; full left hand not tipped, right hand fingerless, hand sewed warranted.
Per pair $1.50
Extra by mail, 10 cents
48156 Boys' Gloves, fingerless, open backs padded .... .20
Short Fingers, Extra by mail
48149

regarded as well-earned battle scars and tell-tale signs of a player's brawn and guts, are cited by supporters as reasons for the ball glove's necessity. Jake Goodwin, shortstop for Lesterville, shamelessly admits he is in favor of the new accessory: "Day in, day out, your hands get really torn up and it is hard to grip the bat tightly with all the bandages." Most fans and players argue that swollen hands and jammed fingers are part of the sport, badges of honor worn proudly by our summer warriors. "It's a man's game after all," says one fan, "and anyone who disagrees can start a splinter collection on the bench." This sentiment is not limited to the stands. Ronald Ferguson, veteran catcher for Dunston, is equally adamant: "It gets a lot easier after three innings or so because the swelling numbs your hands and tends to act like cushioning. It ain't nothing to get bothered over, nothing a real man can't handle." Amazingly, the ball glove, despite overwhelming, level-headed opposition, seems to be gaining gradual acceptance. What's next? Outfielders with parasols? Helmets for base runners? Women players?

Then while the writhing pitcher ground the ball into his hip,
Defiance gleamed in Casey's eye, a sneer curled Casey's lip.

And now the leather-covered sphere came hurtling through the air,
And Casey stood a-watching it in haughty grandeur there.

PUBLISHED EVERY MON
CHICAGO, ILLINOIS

LETTERS TO THE EDIT

Sir:

I would like to re disagree with your absolutely absurd sugg lifting the overhand would be good for the delivery has been ba baseball for some time good reason! Any thinking should realize that the offense will suffer greatly should the ban be lifted and the game will be stripped of any semblance of fair play. With such an unlimited sphere of delivery, along with the added power put upon the ball, the overhand pitch gives the defense all the power.

ARTISTICVIEW

Mudville Center Celebration, June 3, 1888

Balloon inflation ceremony.

only possible remedy for this outrageous travesty of justice would be to move the pitcher's box back ten feet from its present position. This would allow the batter to have more time to react and up the probability of actually making contact with the ball.

Certainly, no serious fan of the sport would deny that home runs and line drives are what make baseball exciting--no one goes to the park to see strike outs and no-hitters. Unless the overhand pitch is coupled with the shifted pitcher's box, reinstating the overhand pitch will completely ruin baseball. If it isn't broken, gentlemen...Don't Try To Fix It!

C. Franceschelli

Close by the sturdy batsman the ball unheeded sped—
"That ain't my style," said Casey. "Strike one," the umpire said.

From the benches, black with people, there went up a muffled roar,
Like the beating of the storm-waves on a stern and distant shore.

THE NATIONAL SPORTS REPORTER & GAZETTE

THE PROUD VOICE OF THE GENTLEMAN ATHLETE AND AMATEUR SPORTSMAN THROUGHOUT THE LAND

PUBLISHED EVERY MONDAY FROM CHICAGO, ILLINOIS MAY 22, 1888

EDITORIAL

THE CLEAR AND CALM voice of reason is finally making itself heard amidst the raucous disputes which so often disrupt our pleasure in attending games of baseball. A majority of managers and team owners appear to be ready to accept what to most of us has long seemed inevitable: the game requires more than one umpire on the field. How often have we been amused and frustrated by the almost comic and quixotic maneuvering of the umpire when, at the sound of the crack of the bat, he uncoils from his crouch and lopes out into the infield? From his new position he is perhaps better able to referee the base runners' movements, but he is now virtually incapable of accurately determining balls and strikes. The heated disputes which inevitably ensue have only too often interrupted play and led to violent melees on and off the field. The modest investment in a second—or even third—umpire will repay itself a hundredfold in increased fair play and the enjoyment of the sport by all. We discern the only possible disadvantage to be to those fans who have heretofore expressed an ardent desire to kill the umpire; they may soon find it necessary to call for the murder of an entire battalion of officials.

Resolutions Not Passed.

Mr. Fraser of ward 6 introduced the following resolutions:

Whereas, the Co___

"Kill him! Kill the umpire!" shouted some one on the stand;
And it's likely they'd have killed him had not Casey raised his hand.

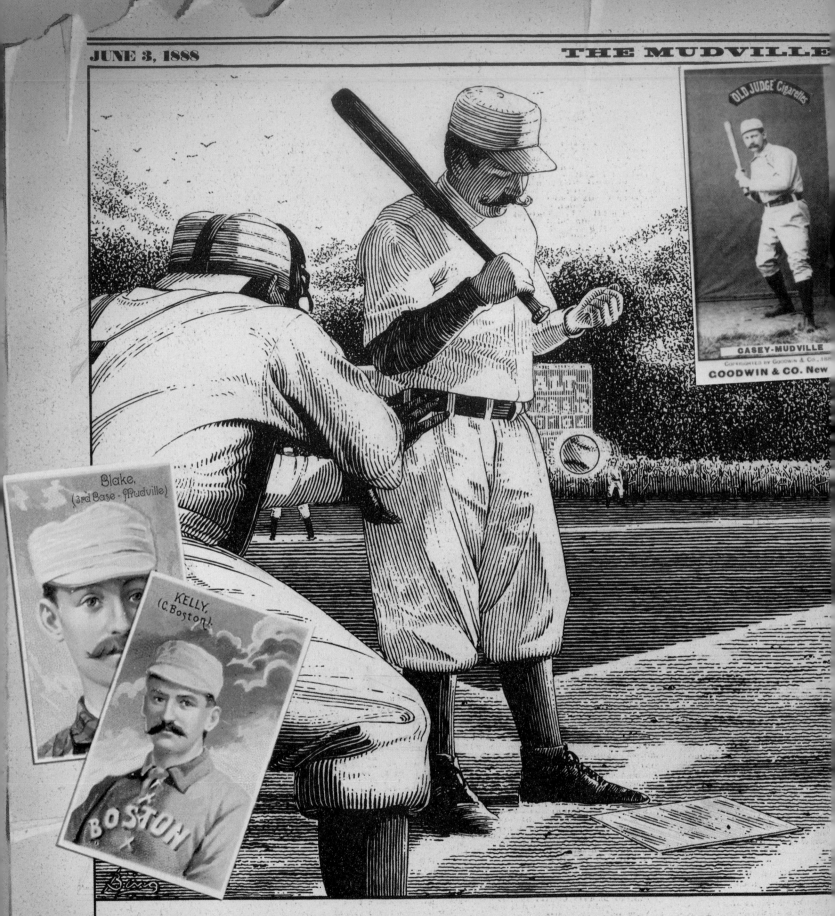

CASEY-MUDVILLE

OLD JUDGE Cigarettes

COPYRIGHTED BY GOODWIN & CO., 188

GOODWIN & CO. New

Blake,
(3rd Base - Mudville)

KELLY
(C. Boston)

BOSTON

With a smile of Christian charity great Casey's visage shone;
He stilled the rising tumult; he bade the game go on;

IN DEFENCE OF THE RESCRIPT.

Sir Joseph Neale McKenna (Liberal)
Comments on the Dublin Meeting.

He signaled to the pitcher, and once more the spheroid flew;
But Casey still ignored it, and the umpire said, "Strike two."

MUDVILLE SCRIMMAGE AT MEMORIAL PARK

BBC

MAY 1888

"Fraud!" cried the maddened thousands, and echo answered fraud;
But one scornful look from Casey and the audience was awed.

display of tri-colored bunting formed an appropriate background for the designs in black and white. These consisted of the colors of the Honourable Artillery Company, the Ancients and the Old Guard, and a portrait of John Milton, a member of the Honourable Artillery Company of Lon.

Wedding at the Church of St. John the Evangelist.

Mrs. Helen Mixter of Beacon street, niece of Mrs. Nathaniel W. Curtis, and Randolph W. Appleton of New York were married at the Church of St. John the Evangelist, on

the slip.

IN HONOR OF R. D. SMITH.

Meeting of the Boston Bar to Take Action on His Death.

There was a meeting of the bar this morn-

brooks they may hold communion with daisies. Perhaps with Claribel and Lillian they will not have time to recall the wrong they have done their fellow by their actions. But time levels all ti and the men unjustly treated may

Barrett

Mudville 11; Salem, 7.
Mudville May 31.—Salem lost today's game on account of an unlucky error by Long in the first inning. Kiley was batted out of the box in the fourth. Burns was also batted hard. Mudville played greatly in the field, but one error, a base on balls, being made. Flynn did fine work in left field, and Rabensky and Casey fielded well. Casey's batting was a feature. The score:

They saw his face grow stern and cold, they saw his muscles strain,
And they knew that Casey wouldn't let that ball go by again.

ert C. Winthrop on the two hundth anniversary of the company, June 1833:

Ballots and bullets—the paper curcy and mettalic basis of a free ple! The former can only be

organist as they proceeded towards the altar, where she was joined by the groom, who had entered another door on the arm of the groomsman, James Appleton. The ushers were Woodbury Kane, H. Curtis, Robert Perkins, William L. Green, Appleton Smith, Walter Bayliss, George Agassiz and C. S. Sprague. The bride wore a robe

of the many temptations to enter official life. He has left a brilliant reputation.
H. C. Hutchins was chosen chairman, and C. A. Prince secretary. William G. Russell then offered a resolution that a committee of five be appointed by the chair to prepare a suitable expression of the sense of the bar upon the character of the deceased

tory—if it could be called a victory—had been won by the party who had brought politics into the fight. The responsibility rested with the Republican party. The contest which had been made would be prob

DUNLAP,
(CAPT, PITTSBURG).

The sneer is gone from Casey's lip, his teeth are clenched in hate;

MUDVILLE

He pounds with cruel violence his bat upon the plate.

T. Sutherland

And now the pitcher holds the ball, and now he lets it go,

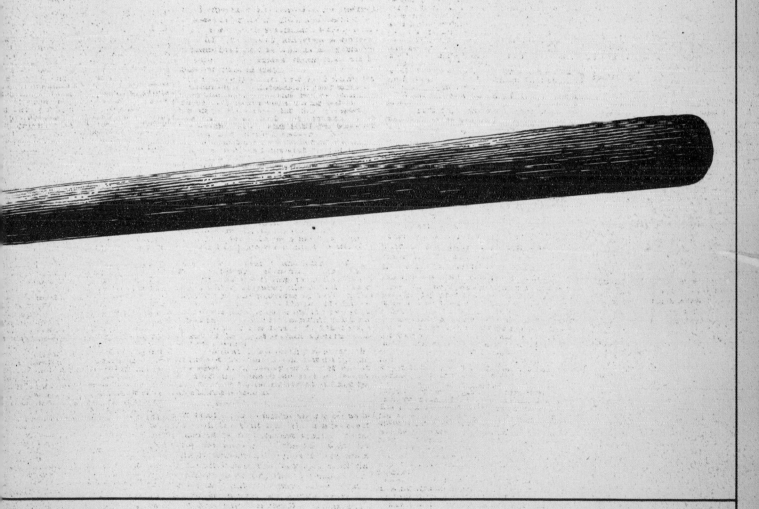

And now the air is shattered by the force of Casey's blow.

the Republicans a good deal of if they had yet got down to seriously consider it. But I don't hear much in either party about the prohibition matter this year. Now then a Democrat will say to my Republican friend that "your party will only two issues after a time, prohibition and protection." But the cheer arose

peculiar aspects to the vice president situation. For a year there have been two or three active and aggressive candidates in the field for this place, that is generally unsought; but there has been no national interest in these rather local characters and their aspirations. Nobody cares particularly for Gray, who has been the leading candidate. He is not a figure in the

COLUMBUS, June 2.—A number of delegates to the Democratic national convention called at Senator Thurman's residence this afternoon, prior to leaving for St. Louis, but no meeting was held relative to taking action towards his support for vice president. Only about one-half the delegation was here. Judge Sherman will not go to St. Louis.

ance at the Country Club races yesterday, accompanied by Lady Middleton.

Prominent among the military men at Young's are General John H. Reed of Cadiz and Colonel Harry Hale of Bradford. Both gentlemen attended the reception in Music Hall last night in honor of our friends and

Oh, somewhere in this favored land the sun is shining bright;
The band is playing somewhere, and somewhere hearts are light;

And somewhere men are laughing, and somewhere children shout;
But there is no joy in Mudville—mighty Casey has struck out.

TOM REED'S OPPONENT.

Mr. Emery Favors Cleveland and Expects to See Thurman Nominated.

SANFORD, Me., June 2.—Hon. William Emery, whom the Democrats of the first district will support for Congress next September, on being questioned by a GLOBE reporter regarding his opinions of the com...

EDITOR'S NOTE:

In order to achieve the feel of a newspaper published in the late Nineteenth Century, great care has been taken to use only fonts equivalent to those that might have been readily available to the compositor of a small town newspaper of the era.

We are particularly fortunate to have had as a resource the collection of historical fonts collected by the Walden Font Company of Winchester, Massachusetts.

Every reasonable attempt has been made to create a seamless tapestry of the real and the fictional, with the modern techniques of photo manipulation and the skill of a gifted designer permitting an unparalleled flexibility in interposing imaginary characters, names and memorabilia into a realistic setting.

The articles "reproduced" from periodicals such as The National Sports Reporter & Gazette and various newspapers in the Mudville area rolled off presses which exist only in the imagination of their creators. They do, however, seek to accurately reflect and articulate actual issues of the day.

It seems only fitting that the figure of Casey is so inextricably woven into the fabric of our history that the Library of Congress--that arbiter of last resort of the classification of books--should have formally and

Remington

STANDARD

Typewriter.

WYCKOFF, SEAMANS & BENEDICT, 327 Broadway, New York, Boston, Mass.; Philadelphia, Pa.; Washington, D. C.; Baltimore, Md.; Chicago Ill.; St. Louis, Mo.; Indianapolis, Ind.; Minneapolis, Minn.; St. Paul, Minn.; Kansas City, Mo.; Denver, Col.; Cincinnati and Cleveland, O.; London, England. NOTE.—Our unqualified challenge for a test of all Writing Machines respectfully unaccepted. Send for copy if interested.

At 1 o... in... quiet... have appear... The Penns... tendered the gene... should at any time... special train to bring Dr. ... delphia to Washington.

permanently assigned to him a date of birth, of death, and a profession.

Casey stands as a heroic reminder that the blurring of fact and fancy, reality and imagination, resides at the core of the American experience.

The final images delivered to the printer were prepared entirely digitally: the artist's illustrations were scanned and then merged with the ancillary images which had been manipulated--or even created--digitally using a variety of graphics software programs including Illustrator, Quark XPress, and Photoshop. A single illustrated spread may be the result of "sandwiching" as many as twenty layers of design elements: type, hand-drawn art, baseball ephemera, and background illustrations; the amount of data needed to describe even one such spread considerably exceeds the information required to print out a very generously-sized encyclopedia.

The black-and-white illustrations were drawn using pen, ink, and brush on white (uninked) scratch board. The newspaper and scrapbook background were created through a series of complex operations involving mirrored photocopies on acetate, 100% cotton-rag watercolor paper soaked in warm acetone baths and watercolors.